OUT of TOWN

Oliver Presl

OUT of TOWN

Oliver Preston

BEVERSTON PRESS

For Omi and Oompah

First published in Great Britain in 2010 by
BEVERSTON PRESS

Tetbury, Glos GL8 8TT

British Library cataloguing in Publication Data
A catalogue record for this title is available from The British Library

ISBN 978-0-9549936-2-7

Designed by boinggraphics.co.uk 01273 600978
Printed by Gutenberg Press, Malta

INTRODUCTION

G. K Chesterton wrote of the cartoonist H.M Bateman, *'If we all know now, at last, where we are really going to, and where science and statesmanship are leading us; and if it is quite obviously to an enormous lunatic asylum, let us at least, by the grace of God, go there in company with a man who has a sense of humour.'*

These strip cartoons were drawn over the past five years for *The Field Magazine* and *Cotswold Life*. During this time the British countryside has been under sustained attack, with government policies negligent towards farming, and hostile towards field sports. More than ever our rural way of life in Britain is misunderstood; our market towns are being denigrated to a boutique shopping experience, and the closure of pubs and stores and post offices in villages and hamlets has led to communities which do not commune. Neighbours are not neighbourly, and road traffic and house building are blighting our green and pleasant land. Yet out in the sticks the locals 'keep buggering on', and by and large with a healthy dollop of our great British sense of humour, they are still able - thankfully - to see the funny side of life.

Meanwhile in London, every friday night a pilgrimage 'out of town' carries on regardless. Like homing pigeons, families brave the terrible traffic, and exit the city for a'fix' of the countryside, to visit friends and relatives, have weekends away or just return to their roots for a couple of days. They soak up country life with a muddy walk here, a roaring fire there, and pints in pubs and sunday roasts. The interreaction between city folk and country dwellers often leads to misunderstandings about 'the right way' of doing things, and the ability of the former to do things 'the wrong way' is inevitably for me a great source of cartoon fun!

I am so lucky to have been born with some social observation, and the ability to scribble. I live in the Cotswolds yet have a weekly foray up to 'town', to friends or clients in London or catching the latest exhibition at the Cartoon Museum in Bloomsbury. If I spend too long in the sticks I develop mild log cabin fever, but after a day in London I quickly yearn for the Cotswolds. There is no warning when a cartoon idea will strike. Travelling in the fast lane of the M4 motorway, a sleepless moment at four o'clock in the morning , whilst walking the dog, out shooting, or in the bath. There is always a mad scramble for a piece of paper to record the revelation. Often the illegible scrawl is indecipherable, or in the cold light of day a very poor joke, but sometimes there are gems to be worked on, and worked up, sent in to the magazines and hopefully published.

A favourite saying of mine is by Victor Borge, who said, 'Laughter is the closest distance between two people.' These cartoons present only a small snapshot of country life, but I hope you enjoy the humour, smile or maybe laugh out loud, and share the drawings with your friends and family.

OLIVER PRESTON

"The guest from hell"

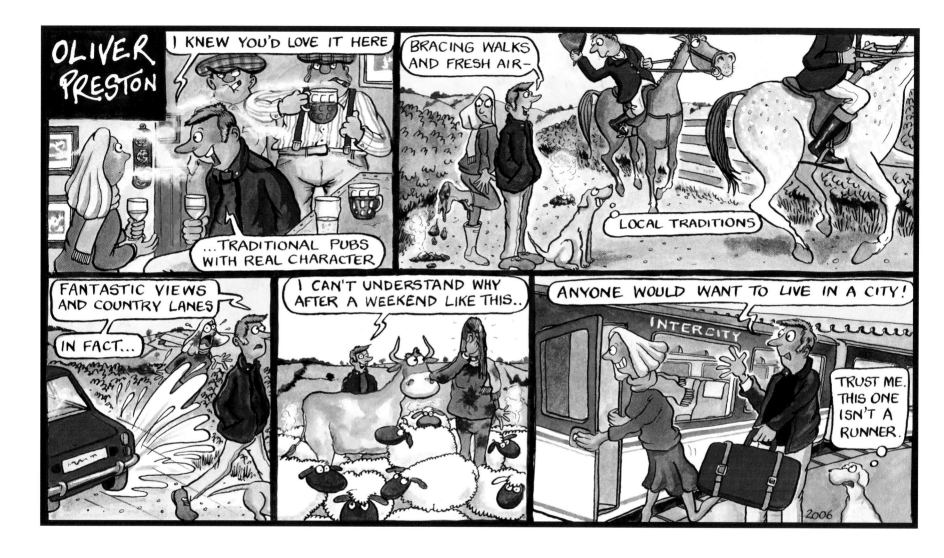

OLIVER PRESTON
HE REALLY LOVES THE FESTIVAL –
ALL YEAR HE LOOKS FORWARD TO CHELTENHAM
THE ROAR OF THE CROWDS, THE ATMOSPHERE, THE SENSE OF OCCASION –
SO THIS YEAR WE'VE GOT HIM REALLY FIT.....
..... HE'S RUNNING WELL, PASSED THE MEDICAL, HIS COAT'S IN GOOD CONDITION
WHAT'S THE BETTING ?
HONESTLY ?
3/08
I'D SAY THE BETTING WAS HE'LL GET PLASTERED WITH HIS IRISH FRIENDS ON THE FIRST TWO DAYS....
...HE'LL BE OUT EVERY NIGHT...
....AND HE WON'T BE THERE FOR THE GOLD CUP. HE WON'T DO THE DISTANCE
I'VE STUDIED HIS FORM

YOUR GRACE....

by OLIVER PRESTON

IT'S NOT REMOTELY FUNNY.

THIS IS 'Chanel'

CHELSEA FLOWER SHOW

IT **WAS** MY OUTFIT FOR ROYAL ASCOT, WIMBLEDON AND HENLEY...

06/09

"What an amazing coincidence. I'm looking at your file as we speak."

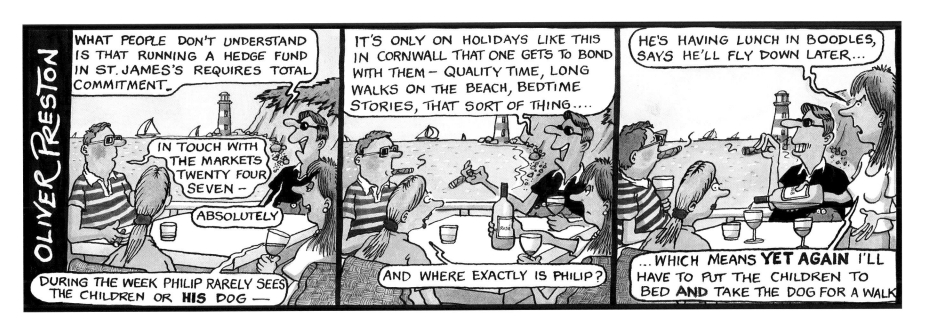

"Great news. Someone's taken the cottage."

"Sox Hunting"

"The Pheasants' Chorus"

ACKNOWLEDGEMENTS

Illustration Acknowledgements

The Field Magazine, Cotswold Life Magazine, BBC Country File Magazine, The Polo Magazine, The Racing Magazine and The Countryside Alliance

By the same author
Shall we join the Men ? (2005) Beverston Press
Hitting the Slopes (2008) Beverston Press

With Alistair Sampson
Liquid Limericks (2001) Robson Books
Larder Limericks (2004) Robson Books

With Charlie Ottley
Modern Cautionary Verses (2006) Constable Robinson

With Rosie Nickerson
How to be Asked Again (2009) Quiller Books

My thanks to Simon Russell at Boing Graphics (01273 600978) for the design and layout preparation and Bobby Blackstock at The Gutenberg Press, Malta, for printing and advice.
Thank you to Arabella Parr at Beverston Press, and Rebecca Hawtrey, Art Editor at The Field Magazine, and Mike Lowe, Editor of Cotswold Life.
To Vivien, Amber and Rex my thanks for being a family of cartoon ideas, capers, and captions.

Prints available from *Out of Town*
Visit: www.beverstonpress.com